PRACTISE TOGETHER SERIES

TABLES 1

2, 3, 4, 5 and 10 times tables

Richard Dawson

A Piccolo Original
Piccolo Books

Draw two fish in each jar . . . complete the number sentences, then do the sums!

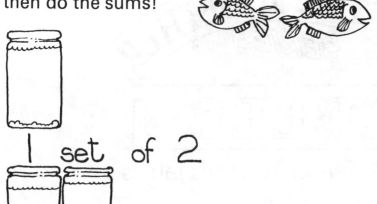

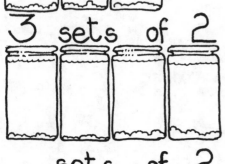

1 set of 2 $1 \times 2 = \boxed{2}$

2 sets of 2 $2 \times 2 = \boxed{4}$

3 sets of 2 $3 \times 2 = \boxed{6}$

sets of 2 $4 \times 2 = \boxed{8}$

sets of 2 $5 \times 2 = \boxed{10}$

sets of 2 $6 \times 2 = \boxed{12}$

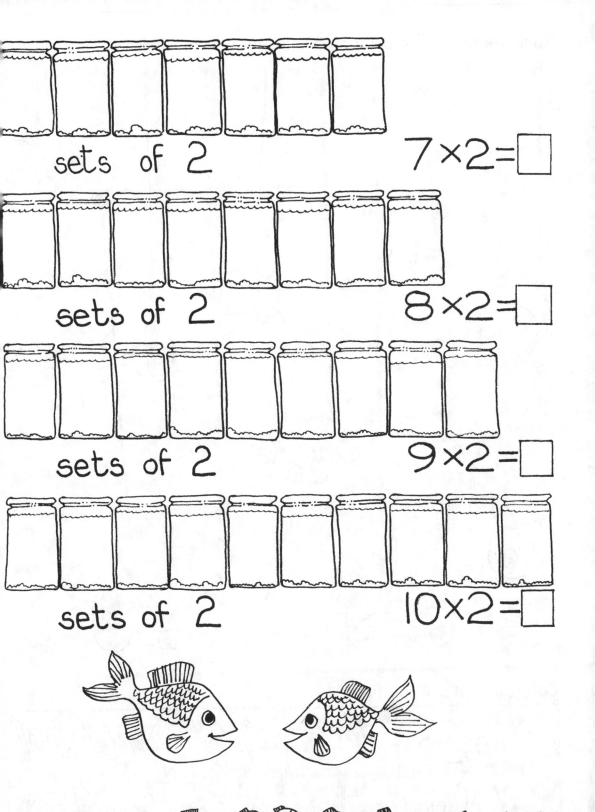

sets of 2 $7 \times 2 = \boxed{}$

sets of 2 $8 \times 2 = \boxed{}$

sets of 2 $9 \times 2 = \boxed{}$

sets of 2 $10 \times 2 = \boxed{}$

3

Stick the fish on to their own worms.

Carefully cut out the fish.

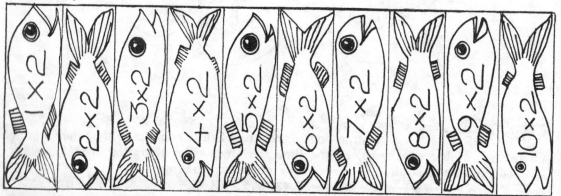

1 x 2 2 x 2 3 x 2 4 x 2 5 x 2 6 x 2 7 x 2 8 x 2 9 x 2 10 x 2

Count in twos and join the dots.

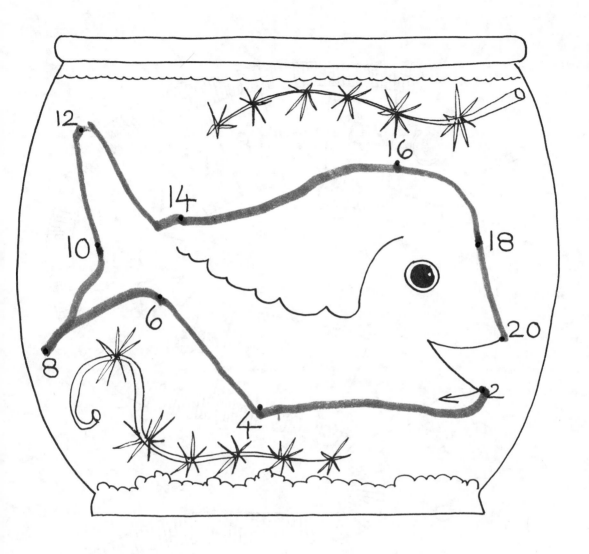

$$1 \times 2 =$$

$$2 \times 2 =$$

$$3 \times 2 =$$

$$4 \times 2 =$$

$$5 \times 2 =$$

$$6 \times 2 =$$

$$7 \times 2 =$$

$$8 \times 2 =$$

$$9 \times 2 =$$

$$10 \times 2 =$$

Count in twos from the tail and colour each square you stop at.

Can you give each seagull its own fish?

Your 5× table is very handy! Count the fingers to answer the sums.

5 →

5 + 5 →

5 + 5 + 5 →

5 + 5 + 5 + 5 →

5 + 5 + 5 + 5 + 5 →

5 + 5 + 5 + 5 + 5 + 5 →

5 + 5 + 5 + 5 + 5 + 5 + 5 →

5 + 5 + 5 + 5 + 5 + 5 + 5 + 5 →

5 + 5 + 5 + 5 + 5 + 5 + 5 + 5 + 5 →

5 + 5 + 5 + 5 + 5 + 5 + 5 + 5 + 5 + 5 →

GUIDELINES: Encourage the children to colour in the fingers, counting the digits in each set. They can then number the palms to count the sets and multiply the number of sets by 5 to find the answer. As children become more fluent with their tables encourage them to think in sets of 5, not count in ones.

Use the 5× table to draw the farmer's route.

Fill in the missing numbers.

$1 \times 5 =$

$\times 5 = 15$

$2 \times \quad = 10$

$5 \times \quad = 25$

$\times 5 = 20$

$6 \times 5 =$

$\times 5 = 35$

$8 \times 5 =$

$0 \times 5 =$

$\times 5 = 50$

$9 \times \quad = 45$

11

Fill in the missing numbers to complete the sums.

$5 = \quad \times 5$

$10 = \quad \times 5$

$15 = \quad \times 5$

$\quad = 4 \times 5$

$\quad = 5 \times 5$

$\quad \times 5 = 30$

$7 \times 5 =$

$\quad \times 5 = 40$

$\quad \times \quad = 45$

$\quad \times 5 = 50$

Use your 5× table to fill in the numbers on the tractor wheel.

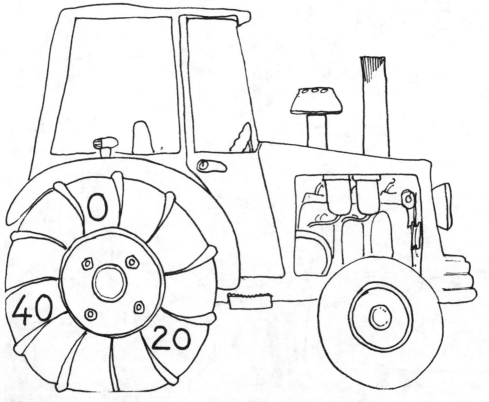

Answer the sums . . . then look for your answers in the picture and colour those shapes pink.

$$1 \times 5 =$$
$$2 \times 5 =$$
$$3 \times 5 =$$
$$4 \times 5 =$$
$$5 \times 5 =$$

$$6 \times 5 =$$
$$7 \times 5 =$$
$$8 \times 5 =$$
$$9 \times 5 =$$
$$10 \times 5 =$$

27 67 3 49 81 63 48 26 9 10 5 35 15 21 16 45 50 30 26 40 25 20 32 32 24 36 19 42

Fill the cups from the correct teapot.

Start at the arrows and follow the number patterns to draw the pictures.

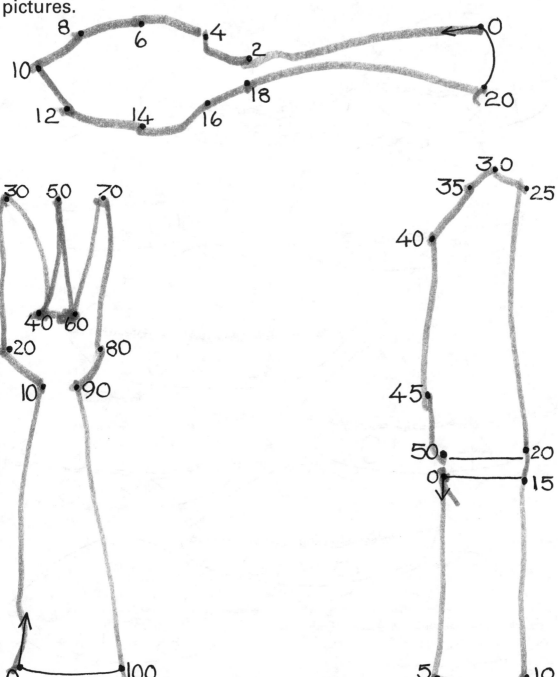

Cut out the apples and stick them in the right pie.

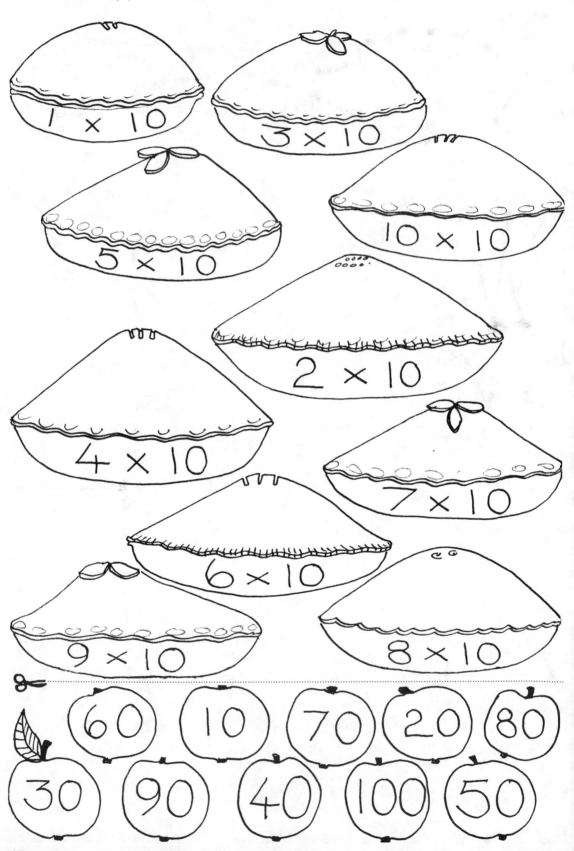

1 × 10

3 × 10

5 × 10

10 × 10

2 × 10

4 × 10

7 × 10

6 × 10

9 × 10

8 × 10

60   10   70   20   80

30   90   40   100   50

Can you put the fillings in the sandwiches by answering the sums?

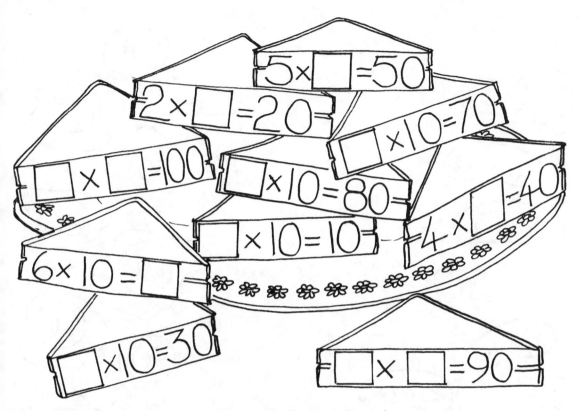

Start at 10 and count in tens to finish the picture.

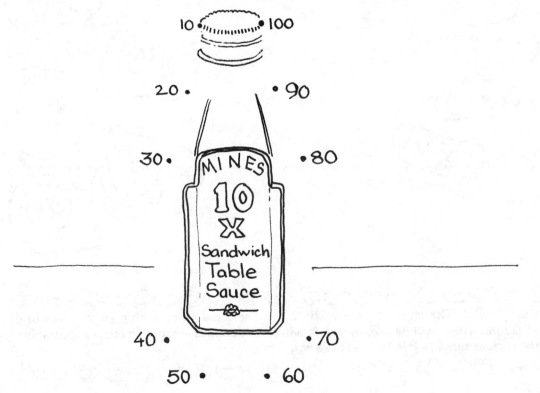

Join the eggs to the sausages.

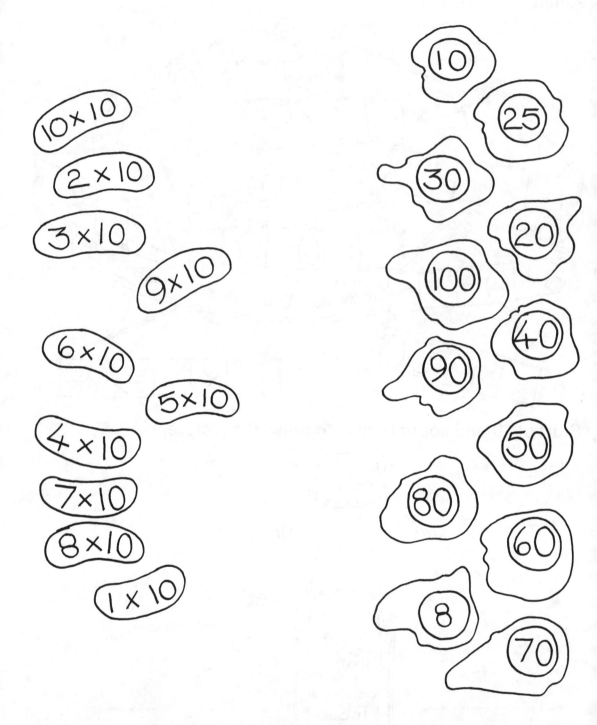

10 × 10

2 × 10

3 × 10

9 × 10

6 × 10

5 × 10

4 × 10

7 × 10

8 × 10

1 × 10

10

25

30

20

100

40

90

50

80

60

8

70

Follow the 10× table to plot the milkman's route.

Join each car to the correct petrol pump.

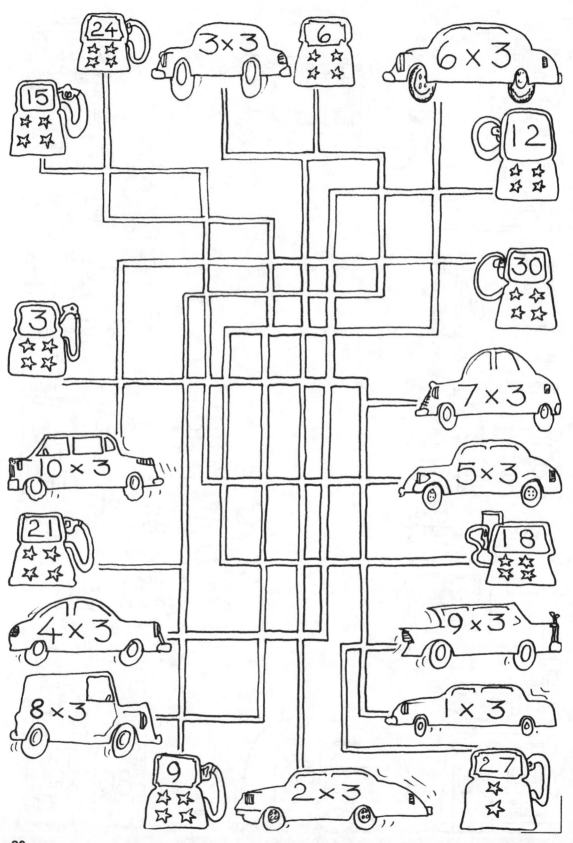

How quickly can you move around the airfield? Answer the sums on your way!

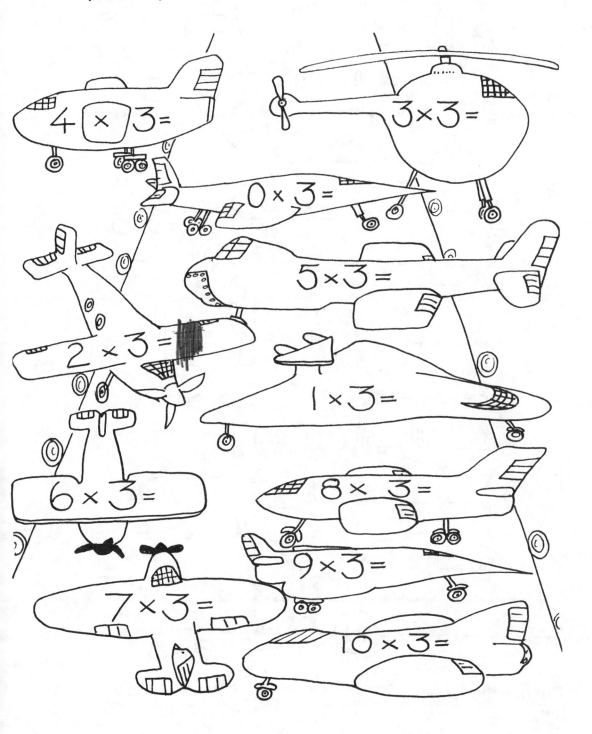

$4 \times 3 =$

$3 \times 3 =$

$0 \times 3 =$

$5 \times 3 =$

$2 \times 3 =$

$1 \times 3 =$

$6 \times 3 =$

$8 \times 3 =$

$9 \times 3 =$

$7 \times 3 =$

$10 \times 3 =$

Stick the wheels back on the right cars.

2×3

7×3

9×3

6×3

5×3

3×3

4×3

10×3

1×3

8×3

Cut out the wheels.

3   9   15   21   27
6   12   18   24   30

Tie up each boat to its own buoy.

Join the stars to the correct sum.

Answer the sums . . .

$1 \times 3 =$ 3
$2 \times 3 =$
$3 \times 3 =$
$4 \times 3 =$
$5 \times 3 =$

Know your 3x table?

$6 \times 3 =$
$7 \times 3 =$
$8 \times 3 =$
$9 \times 3 =$
$10 \times 3 =$

. . . and fill in the table.

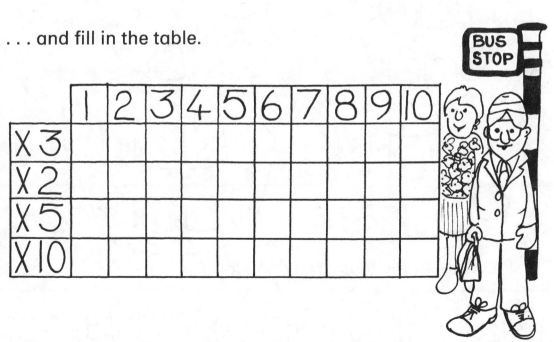

	1	2	3	4	5	6	7	8	9	10
X 3										
X 2										
X 5										
X 10										

Can you find the missing teeth from the smiles? Stick in the teeth that have fallen out.

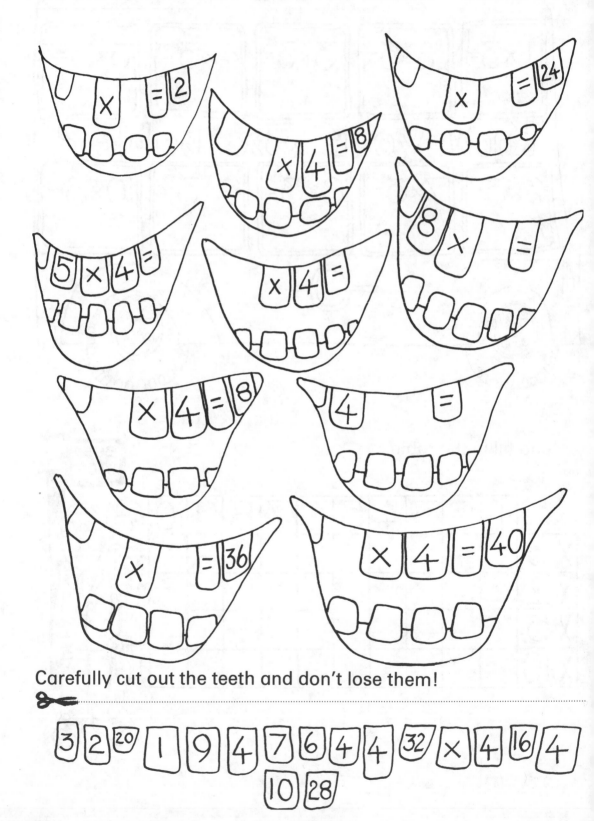

Carefully cut out the teeth and don't lose them!

Put the toothpaste on its own brush.

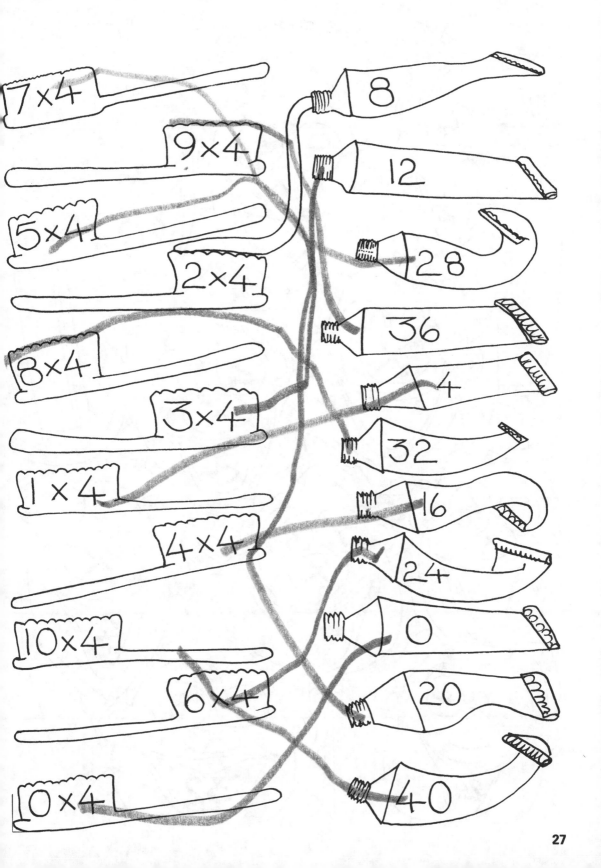

Fill in the clowns' faces by finishing the sums.

Use the 4× table at the top and the 3× table at the bottom to finish the picture.

Climb each tree with the 5, 2, 10, 3 and 4× tables.

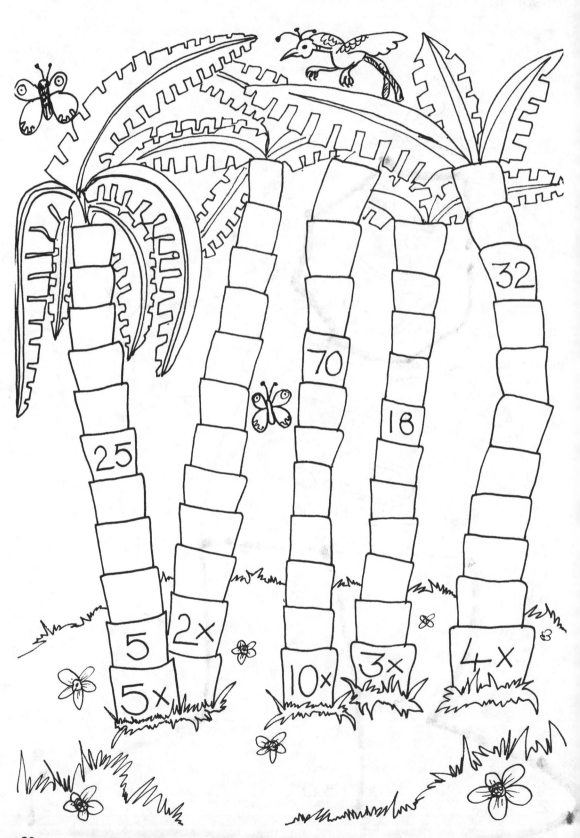

Here are the 2, 3, 4, 5 and 10 times tables in full in case you need them. It's useful to learn them by heart.

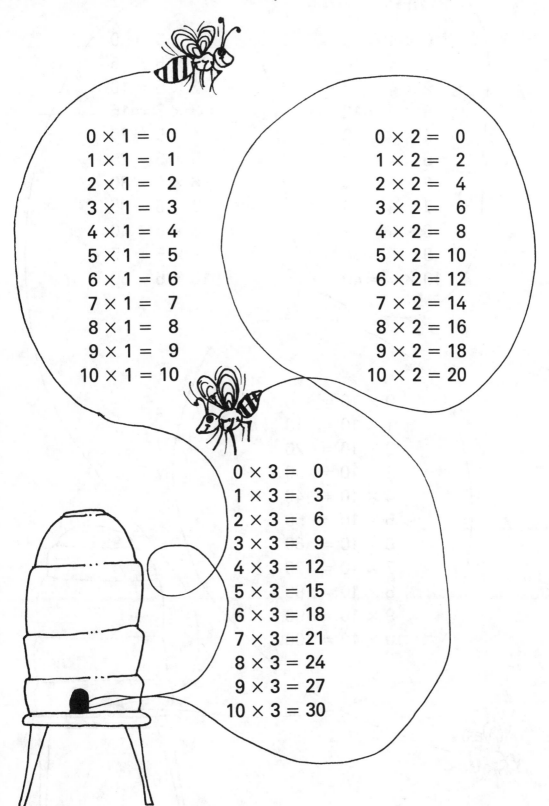

0 × 1 = 0	0 × 2 = 0
1 × 1 = 1	1 × 2 = 2
2 × 1 = 2	2 × 2 = 4
3 × 1 = 3	3 × 2 = 6
4 × 1 = 4	4 × 2 = 8
5 × 1 = 5	5 × 2 = 10
6 × 1 = 6	6 × 2 = 12
7 × 1 = 7	7 × 2 = 14
8 × 1 = 8	8 × 2 = 16
9 × 1 = 9	9 × 2 = 18
10 × 1 = 10	10 × 2 = 20

0 × 3 = 0
1 × 3 = 3
2 × 3 = 6
3 × 3 = 9
4 × 3 = 12
5 × 3 = 15
6 × 3 = 18
7 × 3 = 21
8 × 3 = 24
9 × 3 = 27
10 × 3 = 30

0 × 4 = 0	0 × 5 = 0
1 × 4 = 4	1 × 5 = 5
2 × 4 = 8	2 × 5 = 10
3 × 4 = 12	3 × 5 = 15
4 × 4 = 16	4 × 5 = 20
5 × 4 = 20	5 × 5 = 25
6 × 4 = 24	6 × 5 = 30
7 × 4 = 28	7 × 5 = 35
8 × 4 = 32	8 × 5 = 40
9 × 4 = 36	9 × 5 = 45
10 × 4 = 40	10 × 5 = 50

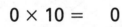

0 × 10 = 0
1 × 10 = 10
2 × 10 = 20
3 × 10 = 30
4 × 10 = 40
5 × 10 = 50
6 × 10 = 60
7 × 10 = 70
8 × 10 = 80
9 × 10 = 90
10 × 10 = 100

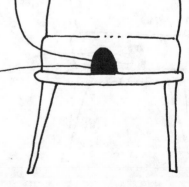